CW00545100

Story by
Toren Smith and Adam Warren

Art by
Adam Warren

Characters and Situations Created by
Haruka Takachiho

Lettering by
L Lois Buhalis and Tom Orzechowski

Published by Manga Publishing Ltd., 40 St Peters Road, London W6 9BD. First edition published September 1995.

British Library Cataloguing in Publication Data. A catalogue record for this book is available from the British Library.

ISBN 1 900097 04 4

CHAPTER ONE

3

4

"LUTHER?"

BIOLOGICALS

YO, BOSS...

RUN INTA A LITTLE *PROBLEM* HERE.

WE FOUND O'DONNELL'S *TISSUE SAMPLES* AND ALL...

...BUT HIS TECHS ALREADY GREW A *CLONE* OUTTA THEM.

CAUTION CRYOGENIC STORAGE

TOTALLY *FINISHED*, TOO, BOSS-- JUST *WAITIN'* FOR A BRAINCHIP.

TOO BIG TA *HAUL*, SO I WAS WONDERIN' WHA--

Oh.

VAPORIZE THAT SUCKER... RIGHT.

YEAH, I KINDA *FIGURED* THAT, BOSS. LUTHER OUT.

OKAY, GUYS. GRAB THEM SAMPLES AN' CLEAR.

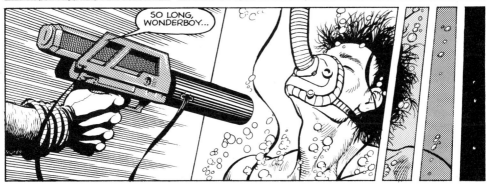

SO LONG, WONDERBOY...

A.D. 2141--MANKIND HAS STEADILY EXPANDED INTO SPACE. OVER 3,000 WORLDS HAVE BEEN TERRAFORMED AND COLONIZED... AND MOST OF THEM ARE MEMBERS OF THE BENEVOLENT, PEACE-LOVING UNITED GALACTICA, ETC., ETC., ETC...

:Yawn:

BET YOU'VE HEARD ALL THAT BEFORE, huh?

HEY!

OOF

WATCH WHERE YOU'RE GOING...

ANYWAY, WHAT'S IMPORTANT IS THAT THE PLANETARY AUTHORITIES SOMETIMES RUN INTO PROBLEMS THEY CAN'T HANDLE.

WHA--!

THAT'S WHERE THE 3WA--THE WORLDS WELFARE WORK ASSOCIATION--COMES IN.

JERK!

BULKHEAD 5

WHAT'S HIS HURRY?!

GET OUT OF MY WAY!

THE PLANETARY AUTHORITIES CAN PETITION THE 3WA FOR HELP.

BULKH

MOVE!

THIS HELP--IF GIVEN-- COMES IN THE FORM OF A TEAM OF PEOPLE SPECIALLY RECRUITED AND TRAINED FOR WORK WITH THE 3WA.

THESE PEOPLE ARE CALLED TROUBLE CONSULTANTS.

PROBLEMS USUALLY MEANING CRIME.

?

6

BIOHAZARD

THE *SPECIAL SPACE FORCES* HAVE A NICE COURT-MARTIAL WAITING FOR YOU, HANDSOME...

"LOVELY ANGELS"--?

THEY'RE *SINGERS*...

...SAW 'EM ON 3V LAST WEEK.

MUSTA BEEN A *PORNO*.

OUR *OFFICIAL* CODE NAME IS 'LOVELY ANGELS'--AFTER OUR SPACESHIP, YOU SEE.

WE'VE *NO INTENTION* OF HAVING ANY INNOCENT BYSTANDERS KILLED THIS TIME, SO JUST COME ALONG QUIETLY, ALL RIGHT?

Oh, YEAH... *RIGHT,*

PROBABLY EASIER TO COUNT THE *SURVIVORS* THAN THE *CORPSES* WHEN THE *DIRTY PAIR* IS INVOLVED!

NOOOO!

EEEYAAA

HELP!

RUN AWAY!

HOWEVER, SOME INSENSITIVE TYPES HAVE NICKNAMED US 'THE DIRTY PAIR'--A NAME WE *HATE*, BY THE WAY.

NO...! BUT... BUT *WAIT*...

WE...WE'RE NOT *LIKE* THAT...

THEY TAGGED US WITH THAT LABEL BECAUSE SOME--*SOME* OF OUR CASES SEEM TO ESCALATE INTO, WELL, *CHAOS* AND *DESTRUCTION.*

B

HEY, *BABES*...

...CHECK *THIS* OUT...

GENUINE **SEREC** FRAG GRENADE-- NICE, huh?

FIGURE YOU BETTER LET ME--

KEI!

HGGAKK

HOOOM

WELL... ALL RIGHT... **MOST** OF OUR CASES END UP THAT WAY, I GUESS.

BEEP

BEEP

BEEP

BOK

BOK

EEEEE

NNNGRAAA!

EXPLOSIONS, INFERNOS... COUPLE THOUSAND CASUALTIES HERE AND THERE...

KCHAK

OOOH! SPEC/FORCE MODS!

!

...AND, INCIDENTALLY...

...A **SOLUTION** TO EVERY CASE.

WHSSSH

IT'S NOT OUR **FAULT** THOSE DISASTERS HAPPEN, THOUGH...

WHA--

...JUST **BAD LUCK**, REALLY.

WHOKK

HUKK

I MEAN, THE CENTRAL 3WA COMPUTER HAS CLEARED US **EVERY** TIME.

CHOK THUMP

WHD

:BEEP BEEP:

IF IT **HADN'T**...

KRAK

HRRGHH

...THEY WOULD HAVE PULLED OUR LICENSES **LONG** AGO, RIGHT?

TIMER IMPACT SAFE

PUSH TO ARM

BEEPBEEP

PACIFICA SECURITY DIRECTOR ALEX GOLDIN RECORDING *NOW*... MEMO 15 DASH LX... ≡Ahem≡ GENTLEMEN, WE HAVE A REAL *SITUATION* HERE.

A *BRAINCHIP* PERSONALITY CONSTRUCT OF ONE OF OUR MAJOR INDUSTRIALISTS HAS BEEN STOLEN.

THE VICTIM IS *KELVIN O'DONNELL*, HEAD OF *O'DONNELL BIOTECHNICS*.

RECENTLY, Mr. O'DONNELL WAS CRITICALLY *WOUNDED* IN A LABORATORY ACCIDENT, BUT BEFORE HIS DEATH, HIS MIND WAS SAFELY ENCODED ONTO A *BRAINCHIP*.

A *CLONE* BODY WAS PREPARED TO RECEIVE THE 'CHIP...

...HOWEVER, BEFORE THE 'CHIP COULD BE IMPLANTED, THE LAB WAS RAIDED BY PERSONS UNKNOWN AND THE 'CHIP SEIZED.

NOW, *HERE* IS OUR PROBLEM...

...O'DONNELL HAS SOME *VERY* POWERFUL ENEMIES.

HE WAS ENGAGED IN THE DEVELOPMENT OF CURES AND PROTECTIVE GEAR FOR *BIOLOGICAL WARFARE WEAPONRY* AND HAD BEEN REPEATEDLY THREATENED, APPARENTLY BY BIOWEAPON INTERESTS-- MANUFACTURERS OR END-USERS, WE DON'T KNOW.

COMPLICATING THE SITUATION IS THE FACT THAT *OUR* ORGANIZATION HAS RECEIVED THINLY VEILED THREATS, AS WELL.

THE SUBSTANCE OF THESE THREATS IS THAT ANY ATTEMPT BY OUR PEOPLE TO RECOVER THE 'CHIP MIGHT RESULT IN THE IMPROMPTU TESTING OF EXPERIMENTAL BIOWEAPONS...

...RIGHT HERE IN PACIFICA!

NOW, OF COURSE WE CAN'T BE SEEN AS YIELDING TO *TERRORISM*...

...BUT NEITHER CAN WE AFFORD TO TAKE RESPONSIBILITY FOR ANY COUNTER-TERRORIST ACTIONS THAT MAY RESULT IN A *BW* INCIDENT.

SO, IN LINE WITH POLICY, WE PETITIONED THE *WWWA* TO SEND A TEAM OF "TROUBLE CONSULTANTS."

HOWEVER, WE FIND OUR PROBLEM HAS BEEN *COMPOUNDED*, RATHER THAN SOLVED.

GENTLEMEN...

...THEY'VE SENT US *THE DIRTY PAIR*.

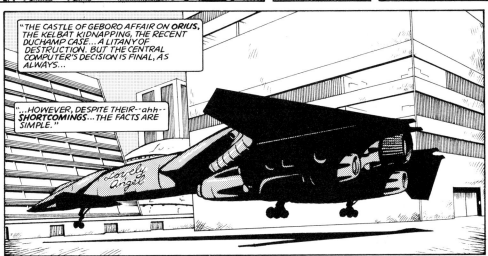

"THE CASTLE OF GEBORO AFFAIR ON *ORIUS*, THE KELBAT KIDNAPPING, THE RECENT DUCHAMP CASE...A LITANY OF DESTRUCTION. BUT THE CENTRAL COMPUTER'S DECISION IS FINAL, AS ALWAYS..."

"...HOWEVER, DESPITE THEIR--ahh-- *SHORTCOMINGS*...THE FACTS ARE SIMPLE."

IF THE TERRORISTS *DO* RELEASE EXPERIMENTAL BIOWEAPONS, THIS PLANET WILL BECOME A *STERILE DESERT*.

WHEREAS, WITH THE INVOLVEMENT OF THE *DIRTY PAIR*, THERE IS A CHANCE--A *REMOTE* POSSIBILITY--THAT *SOME* PEOPLE MAY BE LEFT ALIVE.

WE HAVE TO PLAY THE ODDS, GENTLEMEN...

...GOD HELP US.

13

...AFTER THAT ACCIDENT, THIS GOLDIN ISN'T GOING TO BE VERY HAPPY TO SEE US.

NOT THAT HE WOULD HAVE BEEN, ANYWAY.

BUT IT'D BE NICE IF THIS BRIEFING COULD SOMEHOW GO SMOOTHLY...

...LIKE MAYBE YOU COULD, SAY, NOT LAUGH AT THE POOR GUY.

YEAH? HOW ABOUT FALLING ASLEEP DURING THE BRIEFING?

I RECALL YOU DOING THAT ONCE, Ms. DILIGENCE...

THAT WAS DIFFERENT, AND YOU KNOW IT. ANYWAY, COULD YOU JUST PRETEND THAT YOU'RE PAYING ATTENTION, EVEN IF HE'S NOT VERY GOOD LOOKING?

ALL RIGHT! ALL RIGHT!

I'LL BEHAVE! STRAIGHT OUT OF THE 3WA TEXTBOOK.

ALERT! EAGER!

ATTENTIV--

≈Yawn≈

...LOCATED HIS BRAINCHIP, THOUGH.

IT'S BEEN TRACED TO THE ESTATE OF HIS MAJOR COMPETITOR IN THE FIELD OF BIOWEAPONS CURE AND PROTECTION...

...ONE ABRAHAM STREIB...A TOP INDUSTRIALIST IN THE LOCAL CLUSTER.

NOW, STREIB HAS MORE AGAINST O'DONNELL THAN JUST BUSINESS RIVALRY.

14

TWO YEARS AGO, STREIB WAS RENDERED **QUADRAPLEGIC** AFTER EXPOSURE TO A BIOWEAPON DURING A LAB ACCIDENT.

THE BIO-AGENT ALSO CHANGED STREIB'S **REJECTION SPECTRUM**-- MAKING IT IMPOSSIBLE FOR HIS BODY TO ACCEPT NEUROGRAFTS-- AND HIS **RIFKIN INDEX**, MAKING HIM UNCLONEABLE.

STREIB REFUSED TO LET THE **BIOCONTROL** INVESTIGATIVE TEAM INTO THE **P5** CONTAINMENT LAB WHERE THE EVENT TOOK PLACE, BUT COVERT AGENTS HAVE UNCOVERED EVIDENCE THAT SEEMS TO LINK **O'DONNELL** WITH THE "ACCIDENT."

NICE PEOPLE.

THOSE ARE THE BASICS OF THE CASE...THE DETAILS AND RAW DATA ARE ON THE CHIP I GAVE YOU.

NOW, IN THE FACE OF THE THREATS WE'VE RECEIVED, OUR DEPARTMENT IS SOMEWHAT RELUCTANT TO GO ANY FURTH··

NOT TO WORRY, Mr. GOLDIN!

WE'RE **NEVER** RELUCTANT! THAT'S WHY WE'RE HERE!

YEAH, **NO PROBLEM!** WE'LL JUST POP UP TO STREIB'S ESTATE, CRACK SECURITY, SNAG THE 'CHIP...**FAIT ACCOMPLI,** RIGHT?

WHEN THOSE GUYS HEAR THE **3WA'S** INVOLVED, THEY'LL BACK DOWN, FOR SURE...TRUST ME!

WE'LL DO IT CLEAN AND **QUIET,** TOO, SIR! THEY'LL NEVER KNOW WHAT HIT THEM...!

15

16

Ah, but enough of the *PAST*. Let us discuss the *FUTURE*... More specifically, your *IMMEDIATE* future...

≈CHERK?≈

MY ESTATE ENCOMPASSES A FAIR BIT OF FORESTED GROUNDS...

...AND YOU, MY FRIEND, ARE GOING TO PLAY A LITTLE GAME OF *HIDE AND SEEK* IN THOSE WOODS."

IF YOU COULD ONLY *SPEAK*, I'M *CERTAIN* YOU WOULD ASK, "BUT *WHO* AM I TO PLAY WITH?" ALLOW ME TO SHOW YOU.

LUTHER! LEAD THEM IN!

YOUR *PLAYMATES*-- CUSTOM BIOENGINEERED *WARBEASTS.*

PERFECT KILLING MACHINES, THEIR DEVELOPMENT AND BREEDING *ILLEGAL* ON EVERY INHABITED PLANET IN THE UNITED GALACTICA...NONETHELESS, *VERY* USEFUL FOR *SECURITY PURPOSES.* YOU DOUBTLESS POSSESS -- *POSSESSED*--MORE THAN A FEW, YOURSELF.

SEVERAL OF THESE, *ah, LIVELY* CREATURES WILL BE PURSUING YOU THROUGH THE FOREST.

HRAAAAARRGG

GRRRAAAAARRRRR

V2

PLEASE NOTE THE *VIDEOLINKS* IN THE EYES. THROUGH THOSE, I SHALL BE MONITORING THE HUNT...SO AS TO *SAVOR* THE EXPERIENCE TO IT'S FULLEST EXTENT.

OH, BY THE WAY...

VZZT

GRRHAAARRR

...I ALSO STOLE YOUR *TISSUE SAMPLES.* I EVENTUALLY INTEND TO GROW A CLONE OF YOUR ORIGINAL BODY, THEN IMPLANT IT WITH A COPY OF YOUR BRAINCHIP.

THEN IN ALL LIKELIHOOD, I WILL *TORTURE* IT UNTIL I TIRE OF DOING SO, OR UNTIL IT *EXPIRES.* AFTER ALL, I CAN ALWAYS GROW ANOTHER.

BUT AS FAR AS YOUR GAME OF HIDE AND SEEK GOES, DON'T WORRY...

...YOU'LL HAVE A *FIFTEEN MINUTE* HEAD START.

SQUEEK!

OUR PET, *MUGHI,* IS FROM SOME OBSCURE PLANET WITH AN UNPRONOUNCEABLE NAME. HE'S *HIGHLY* INTELLIGENT--AND HIGHLY *LAZY,* I MIGHT ADD-- BUT VERY HELPFUL TO US.

FOR ONE THING, HE CAN RIP PEOPLE LIMB FROM LIMB-- ALWAYS HANDY, IN OUR LINE OF WORK--AND HIS CLAWS CAN SLICE THROUGH HULLMETAL.

HOWEVER, HE HAS MORE *DELICATE* TALENTS, AS WELL.

USING THE SPINES IN HIS EARS, HE CAN MANIPULATE THE ENTIRE ELECTROMAGNETIC SPECTRUM AT WILL. *NO,* I HAVEN'T THE *SLIGHTEST* IDEA HOW IT WORKS.

GENERALLY SPEAKING, MUGHI HANDLES THE *TECHNOLOGICAL* PROBLEMS THAT CROP UP...

...THEORETICALLY LEAVING *US* FREE TO CONCENTRATE ON SOLVING THE CASE.

FRZZT

GYAAAGHH!

SHOOOM

EVER GIVE ANY THOUGHT TO SHOOTING PEOPLE'S *WEAPONS*, KEI?

HEY... I WAS *AIMING* FOR THE GUN, DAMMIT!

SIGHTS MUST BE OFF.

ANYWAY... WE'RE LOOKING FOR *ANSWERS*, AND, WELL, WE'RE LOOKING AT *YOU*...

HUH! LOOK SOMEWHERE ELSE...I AIN'T TALKIN' TO *YOU*...

YOUR CALL.

MUGHI... *PERSUADE* HIM.

WHSSSH

Huh...? *OW!*

OWW!

...ALL RIGHT! ALL RIGHT!!

HEY...

CHIP'S IN THIS *ANIMAL*, SEE...

...AND THERE'S THIS *HUNT*...!

22

23

SHOOM
Oh, THIS IS JUST GREAT.
HRAARRR HRRRRR RRR
SQKK
HRAAARR
CHAKA CHAKA CHAKA
SHOOOM
HRAARRK!
YOWWRR!
DIE!
SHOOM
DIE!
SHOOOM
WILL YOU @%*?!ING DIE?!

WHAT!?!

KLIK KLIK KLIK

IT'S *NOT* THAT YURI DOESN'T LIKE A GOOD FIGHT *QUITE* AS MUCH AS I DO...

...BUT I MAY *START* A FEW TOO MANY FOR HER *TASTE*, I THINK.

ARR ARR

NICE BEASTIE! HERE, HAVE A *SNACK!*

IMPACT

ANYWAY, A LITTLE *FIREPOWER*, BIT OF HAND-TO-HAND... GETS US OUT OF MOST SCRAPES *EASY.*

SKNCH

BUH KOOM

HUH! I DON'T *BELIEVE* IT!

THAT ACTUALLY *WORKED!*

HEY, *WE* DIDN'T WASTE OUR TIME IN 3WA TRAINING CAMP!

BUT IF THE *USUAL* TECHNIQUES AREN'T WORKING, WE'VE GOT A *TRICK* OR TWO TO FALL BACK ON...

CHAPTER TWO

COMPLICATIONS

...BUT I THINK GOLDIN MAY HAVE BEEN A BIT LOW-KEY IN DESCRIBING STREIB'S END OF OUR LITTLE "BUSINESS RIVALRY."

THERE'VE BEEN MORE THAN A FEW INCIDENTS THAT GOLDIN AND HIS SPOOKS WOULD TURN WHITE TO HEAR ABOUT.

HUH! WELL, MR. O'DONNELL, THAT'S VERY INTERESTING, BUT DIDN'T YOU--

STREIB IS A VICIOUS THUG AND I'VE BEEN DOING NOTHING MORE THAN DEFENDING MYSELF, DESPITE GOLDIN'S OPINION.

IN ANY CASE, MY TECHNICIANS HERE TELL ME STREIB'S GOONS HAVE CLEANED OUT EVERY ONE OF MY TISSUE SAMPLES, AND I'D LIKE YOUR HELP TO GET THEM BACK.

OUR HELP...?!

HEY, THE 3WA SENT US HERE TO RECOVER YOUR BRAINCHIP AND THAT'S ALL.

WHICH WE'VE DONE WITH NO INNOCENT CASUALTIES AND ALMOST NO PROPERTY DAMAGE, I MIGHT ADD.

SORRY, MR. O'DONNELL, BUT OUR JOB HERE IS OVER.

PLEASE, CALL ME KELVIN.

BUT COULDN'T YOU HELP FOR HUMANITARIAN REASONS?

THINK OF ME, TRAPPED FOR THE REST OF MY DAYS IN A SERIES OF UNSATISFACTORY BODIES, WHEN I COULD BE WEARING MY OWN, WHEN I COULD BE WEARING...

...THIS!

HOLD

I'D REALLY HATE TO HAVE TO GET USED TO ANOTHER BODY...

Oh, ABSOLUTELY!

I THINK WE OUGHT TO HELP HIM.

YOU *WOULD*. I COULD HEAR YOUR *HORMONES* KICK IN FROM ACROSS THE ROOM.

OH, YEAH? WELL, YOU'RE RUNNING A *HIGH FEVER* RIGHT NOW, I SEE.

WE'LL GET INTO *SERIOUS* TROUBLE FROM THE 3WA.

AW, C'MON.

OH, ALL RIGHT.

OKAY, KELVIN, WE'RE ON BOARD.

LADIES, I'M *DELIGHTED*. LET ME GIVE YOU A LITTLE BACKGROUND HERE.

AS YOU KNOW, I'M IN THE PROTECTION RACKET-- PROTECTION FROM THE AMAZING RANGE OF BIOCHEM WEAPONS IN USE THESE DAYS.

"SINCE I MUST, BY NECESSITY, WORK WITH A NUMBER OF REALLY FRIGHTFUL SUBSTANCES, LAW REQUIRES THAT I ISOLATE MY DANGEROUS RESEARCH ON AN AIRLESS AND UNINHABITED PLANET. THE PENALTIES FOR NOT DOING SO ARE, TO PUT IT MILDLY, *SEVERE*.

"PACIFICA IS FORTUNATE IN HAVING TWO MEDIUM-SIZED MOONS AVAILABLE-- *TELEK*, THE INNER MOON, ON WHICH STREIB HAS SET UP SHOP; AND *TALLIS*, WHERE MY LAB IS LOCATED."

AS I MENTIONED EARLIER, STREIB HAS BEEN OUT TO RUIN MY BUSINESS FROM DAY ONE, MOSTLY BY ATTEMPTS ON MY LIFE -- WITHOUT ME, THE RESEARCH PROGRAM HERE WOULD FALL APART.

STREIB HAS RIDDLED MY ORGANIZATION WITH SPIES, AND I'VE DONE THE SAME WITH HIS. BASICALLY OUT OF SELF-PRESERVATION.

"A FEW WEEKS AGO, WHILE PREPARING SOME ALTERED BACTERIA FOR *NMR* TESTING, I MADE AN UNPLEASANT DISCOVERY-- ONE OF STREIB'S MINIONS HAD SWAPPED SAMPLES ON ME, AND I GOT NAILED BY A VIAL OF ANTHRAX-LEPROSY ZETA.

BEING UNBELIEVABLY PARANOID FOR SOME REASON, STREIB'S GOT DAMN NEAR MILITARY-LEVEL SECURITY AT HIS LAB HERE.

"FORTUNATELY, MY ASSISTANTS GOT ME HOOKED UP TO A BRAINCHIP SCANNER BEFORE CELLULAR BREAK-DOWN HAD BEGUN. BUT, AS YOU KNOW, STREIB GOT MY 'CHIP AND MY TISSUE SAMPLES BEFORE I COULD BE TRANSFERRED INTO MY CLONE."

THE USUAL LOCKS AND WARDS, OF COURSE. BUT HE'S REAL HEAVY ON PERSONNEL... ROBOTS, BIO-ENGINEERED HUMANS, WAR-BEASTS, A FEW DOZEN MERCENARIES AND ASSORTED RIFF-RAFF, PLUS AN AIR SUPPORT TEAM WITH THREE GUNSHIPS.

HOWEVER, ONE OF MY AGENTS HAS TURNED UP A WEAK SPOT IN THE EXTERNALS. AS LONG AS WE STAY QUIET AND AVOID THE VARIOUS WATCHDOGS, WE SHOULD BE ALL RIGHT.

"WE?" PARDON, BUT WHAT POSSIBLE GOOD WOULD *YOU* BE? A TASTY SNACK FOR STREIB'S WARBEASTS?

IN *THIS* BODY, CERTAINLY...

TIME FOR YOUR OPERATION, SIR.

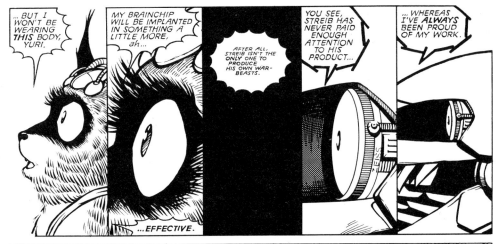

A *GARBAGE* CHUTE?! THAT'S *DISGUSTING!*

AT LEAST IT'S ONLY *KITCHEN* GARBAGE, YURI... IT COULD BE WORSE, LIKE...

I *DON'T* WANT TO HEAR ABOUT IT.

KELVIN, DON'T GET TOO FAR BELOW THE CAMOUFLAGE DRONE...

...ITS *FIELD* IS ONLY GOOD OUT TO FIVE METERS.

AS LONG AS IT WORKS... THERE'S A *LOT* OF DETECTION GEAR UP THERE.

DOWN TO TWO MINUTES ON THE GRAVPACKS, YURI.

NO PROBLEM... I'M ALMOST DONE WITH *MUGHI'S* "LITTLE BLACK BOX" HERE.

O'D

HERE WE GO... GREEN LIGHTS ACROSS THE BOARD.

IT'S INTO STREIB'S *SECURITY LINES*...WE'LL BE INVISIBLE TO ANY OF HIS INTERNAL SENSORS.

HOW ABOUT THE HATCH? LASER THROUGH?

NOT ENOUGH TIME ON THE PACKS. SHAPED CHARGES?

KRNKK!

......

STRANGE... THEY DON'T EVEN HAVE ANY ANTI-PERSONNEL GRIDS INSTALLED... THAT'S *STANDARD* SECURITY.

WELL, I— HUH?

WHY, *KEI*... BEEN HITTING THE CHEESECAKE A LITTLE TOO HARD LATELY, HAVE WE?

I *DON'T* WANT TO HEAR IT, YURI...

*&%#!!

LOOKS LIKE A *DIET* MIGHT BE IN ORDER, *hmmm?*

LOOKS JUST *FINE* TO ME...

UMPH! *YU*RIII...!

SEC. A

SEC. A

KRANG

C'MON-- SOMETHING'S UP!

WAIT A SEC-- --THESE ISOLATION CHAMBERS--

≈ULK!≈

LISTEN, TIGER... YURI DOESN'T GET EXCITED OVER NOTHING.

LET'S MOVE IT!

KEI...

WHAT'S UP?

WELL, WE'VE GOT SOME SERIOUS TROUBLE HERE...

... STREIB'S SHIPPED YOUR TISSUE SAMPLES TO HIS LAB ON TELEK.

GAAAH... THAT'S A PROBLEM, ALL RIGHT...

YOU'VE GOT MORE IMMEDIATE PROBLEMS THAN THAT, I'M AFRAID...

IT'S STREIB...!

Oh, GREAT...

YOUR LITTLE ECM BOX PERFORMED SURPRISINGLY WELL, I MUST ADMIT... YOU'VE GOTTEN A LITTLE FARTHER THAN ANTICIPATED, EVEN THOUGH WE WERE EXPECTING YOU.

YOU SEE, DEAR GUESTS, THAT "WEAK SPOT" IN MY SECURITY WAS DESIGNED TO ATTRACT SUCH ATTENTION.

?!?

LAB A

KELVIN! WHICH WAY TO THE HANGAR?!

HERE!

WE'VE GOT TO STEAL ONE OF STREIB'S GUNSHIPS AND GET *OUT* OF HERE!

WHY BOTHER WITH *THAT*?

WHY DON'T YOU JUST CALL MUGHI AND HAVE HIM BRING IN THE *LOVELY ANGEL*?!

LAB A

HAH!

YOU KNOW THAT GREAT LITTLE BLACK BOX HE WHIPPED UP FOR US?

IT'S BLOCKING *OUR* SIGNALS, TOO!

I *SWEAR*, I'M GONNA MAKE A *RUG* OUT OF THAT CREATURE SOME DAY!

THERE'S SORT OF A LOUNGE THROUGH THIS DOOR... WE CUT ACROSS THAT AND TURN RIGHT!

LOUNGE

!

SWISH

41

43

44

45

46

52

CHAPTER THREE

Y-YURI...

...WHAT IS IT...?

IT...

...IT MUST'VE BROKEN IN THE CRASH... I, I DIDN'T NOTICE...

DAMN IT, YURI, WHAT *IS* THAT?!

Oh...

...um, O'DONNELL FOUND IT AT THE LAB...

HE...HE SAID HE COULD USE IT AS EVIDENCE TO *RUIN* STREIB...

Uh, KEI...?

HE SAID THIS IS PROBABLY A *"LETHAL BIOWARFARE AGENT"*...

...AND I'VE BEEN IN CONTACT WITH IT FOR A FEW MINUTES NOW.

I DON'T KNOW HOW IT *SPREADS*, SO YOU'D BETTER GET OUT OF HERE...

...QUICKLY.

B-BUT...

I'M SORRY, KEI...

HEY, *WAIT...!*

YURI... DON'T...

KLIK

SLAM

YURI!

55

OUTBREAK

THMP
THMP
THMP

.....

GREAT. JUST WHAT WE NEEDED.

YURI'S A *DEMENTED PSYCHOPATH.* MORE SO THAN USUAL, I MEAN.

--WAIT. WE STUDIED BIOWEAPONS IN 3WA TRAINING...

...DIDN'T WE...?

WASN'T THERE SOMETHING ABOUT AN--

I WONDER WHAT THAT *BIOWEAP--*

--AGENT, DEPLOYED AGAINST ENEMY TROOP FORMATIONS PRIOR TO, er, COMBAT, WHICH CONVERTS SAID ENEMY INTO, SHALL WE SAY, *DERANGED BERSERKERS*--

~YAWN~

"--JUST AS LIKELY TO KILL EACH OTHER AS THEIR FOES." RIGHT.

NOW... DID IT WEAR OFF, OR DID IT KI- ~ulp~ I CAN'T REMEMBER...

THEN AGAIN, I DIDN'T PASS THAT COURSE.

YURI DID.

~Sigh~ ...

...WONDER IF KELVIN MADE IT...

CAN'T BE DOING ANY WORSE THAN *WE* ARE...

65

67

74

ACTUALLY, KEI, I'M QUITE A BIT FONDER OF *YOUR* ASSETS...

Mmm... REALLY...?

...BUT I THOUGHT YOU W'R *LAUGHING* WHEN I COULDN'T FIT INTO TH' *AIRDUCT* OPENING...

NOT AT *ALL*...

...IN FACT, I TOOK ONE LOOK AT YOU STUCK THERE AND THOUGHT... "I'M IN *LOVE*."

Oooh... WICKED BOY...! S'FUNNY, THOUGH...

...I THOUGHT THE SAME THING WHEN I SAW Y'R *REAL* BODY.

...THAT *WAS* YOURS, RIGH...?

DAMN *STRAIGHT* IT WAS.

FINE BODY TO BE INSIDE, BELIEVE ME.

THEN AGAIN, I COULD PROBABLY SAY THE SAME THING ABOUT *YOURS*.

mmMMmm...

HOW DARE YOU...YOU *CAD*...

KRUNK

SORRY. HARD TO TAKE FLIRTATION SERIOUSLY WHEN I LOOK LIKE *THIS*-- I PROBABLY SHOULDN'T HAVE STARTED IT.

Oh, I DON'T KNOW...

I THINK YOU'RE DOING JUS' *FINE*...

KELVINN...

Hmm...?

...THINK I'M GONNA... *NAP* FOR A BIT...

SORRYYY...

GOOD NIGHT, KEI...

...AND THANK YOU.

AHA...SLEEPING BEAUTY IS AWAKE, EH?

WH--

YOU'RE ON BOARD THE *LOVELY ANGEL*--WARM, SAFE AND ALL THAT. ONCE I FIGURED OUT YOUR COMLINK, MUGHI PICKED US UP IN A FEW MINUTES.

YURI...!

KELVIN...IS...IS SHE--

SHE'S *FINE*, KEI.

SHE'LL BE UP, ABOUT, AND NO DOUBT *WREAKING HAVOC* IN AN HOUR OR TWO.

IT WAS NO GREAT TASK TO CURE HER OF STREIB'S EMBARRASSINGLY CRUDE WORK...

Mm-hmm.

...AFTER ALL, I AM A MEDICAL GENIUS.

THANK YOU, KELVIN. ♡

ANY✳ ANYTIME, KEI...!

Oh, YEAH!

...SO ANYWAY, THAT'S WHAT HAPPENED.

NOW, I FIGURE WE OUGHT TO INFILTRATE STREIB'S MOONBASE, GET YOUR TISSUE SAMPLE, THEN *BLOW UP THE WHOLE DAMN PLACE!!*

SO WHADDA YA SAY?

SOUNDS GOOD TO ME...

Lovely Angel

CHAPTER
FOUR

82

YOU'RE **CERTAIN** THEY'RE **GONE?**

YOU TRACKED THEIR SHIP RETURNING TO **PACIFICA?!**

VERY WELL, THEN. CARRY ON, AND KEEP US POSTED ON ANY FURTHER **OMINOUS OCCUR-ENCES,** WILL YOU?

TELEK BASE OUT.

POST A TECH TEAM TO SWEEP THE SHUTTLE AS **SOON** AS IT LANDS.

I DO **NOT** LIKE THE SOUND OF THIS, M97.

PACIFICA SECURITY DIRECTOR GOLDIN ON LINE **FOUR,** SIR.

THIS IS BOUND TO BE TIRESOME...

Ah, DIRECTOR **GOLDIN**...

... WHAT A **PLEASANT** SURPR--

SAVE IT, STREIB!

YOU'VE GONE **TOO FAR** THIS TIME. SIXTY-THREE CASUALTIES, MILLIONS IN PROPERTY DAMAGE...

... AND **RIGHT** IN THE **CAPITAL,** NO LESS!

ONCE THE AUTHORIZATION COMES IN, I'M SETTING INTO MOTION **THOROUGH** INVESTIGA-TIONS ON YOUR OPERATIONS ON BOTH PACIFICA **AND** TELEK...

... AND I'VE **NO DOUBT** WE'LL FIND **ALL KINDS** OF INTERES--

"SAVE IT," MR. GOLDIN.

OUR **MUTUAL** FRIENDS IN THE GOVERNMENT WOULD FIND SUCH AN INVESTIGATION, ah, **DISPLEASING**...

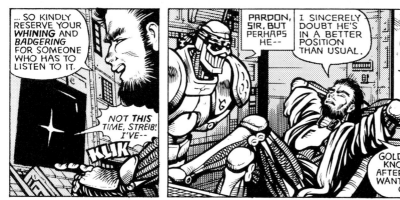

... SO KINDLY RESERVE YOUR *WHINING* AND *BADGERING* FOR SOMEONE WHO HAS TO LISTEN TO IT.

NOT *THIS* TIME, STREIB! I'VE--

KLIK

PARDON, SIR, BUT PERHAPS HE--

I SINCERELY DOUBT HE'S IN A BETTER POSITION THAN USUAL.

GOLDIN AND HIS KEEPERS KNOW THEIR PLACE. AFTER ALL, THEY DON'T WANT ANOTHER *FUNDING* CUT, OR *PURGE*...

... SO, DESPITE THEIR IRRITATING YAMMERING TO THE CONTRARY, THEY'LL LEAVE US *ALONE.*

A MUCH MORE *SIGNIFICANT* CONCERN, HOWEVER, IS O'DONNELL AND HIS "DIRTY PAIR"...

... I RATHER SUSPECT THAT, EVEN AS WE SPEAK, THEY'RE HATCHING SOME *INCONVENIENT* PLOT...

"NOW, LADIES-- STREIB'S BASE ON *TELEK* IS A LOVELY BIT OF *VERY EXPENSIVE* ENGINEERING.

"TO COMPENSATE FOR TELEK'S INSIGNIFICANT GRAVITY, HE BUILT MOST OF HIS LABS AND SUCH IN AN ENORMOUS REVOLVING WHEEL, SORT OF LIKE A SLIGHTLY ANGLED SPACE STATION.

"IT'S BURIED JUST BELOW THE SURFACE OF THE MOON-- *VERY* COMPLEX, *VERY* COSTLY...

"AND I SUSPECT... *VERY* DOOMED."

COMMAND · LIFE SUPPORT · POWER · DOCK TWO · DOCK ONE · STORAGE · RECREATION · ADMINISTRATIVE · BIOLAB Ⓐ · BIOLAB Ⓑ

Remission

86

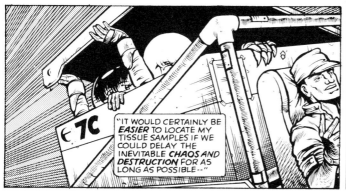

"IT WOULD CERTAINLY BE *EASIER* TO LOCATE MY TISSUE SAMPLES IF WE COULD DELAY THE INEVITABLE *CHAOS AND DESTRUCTION* FOR AS LONG AS POSSIBLE--"

"*INEVITABLE?!?*"

"Er...WELL....IT'S *REALLY* FREQUENT...ISN'T IT...?"

"......."

"YEAH, WELL MAYBE IT IS *KIND* OF INEVITABLE..."

"≋*ahem*≋ WELL, *ANYWAY*...EVEN-TUALLY THE MAGLEV CAR WILL REACH THE WHEEL'S INNER RIM, MATCH VELOCITIES, AND ENTER THE ELEVATOR SHAFT--"

ELEVATOR B

"--DON'T FORGET, DUE TO THE ROTATION, THE GRAVITY IN THE WHEEL IS ONLY FIVE DEGREES OFF HORIZONTAL."

"ONCE INSIDE THE WHEEL, WE HIT THE BIOLAB AREA."

CRYONICS STORAGE AND SUPPLY

7C

8C

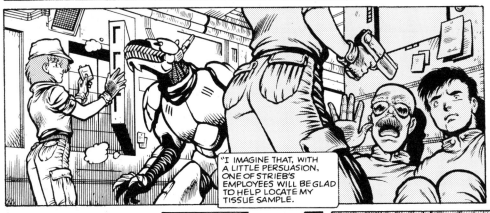

"I IMAGINE THAT, WITH A LITTLE PERSUASION, ONE OF STRIEB'S EMPLOYEES WILL BE GLAD TO HELP LOCATE MY TISSUE SAMPLE."

"YOU KNOW, KEI, I'M *REALLY* LOOKING FORWARD TO HAVING MY OLD BODY BACK."

"WHAT A *COINCIDENCE*, KELVIN..."

O'DONNELL KELVIN A.

"...SO AM I."

"I CAN'T WAIT TO *FINALLY*--"

O'DONNELL KELVIN A.

"DO YOU TWO *MIND?!*"

"OH--SORRY, YURI. GO ON, KELVIN..."

"*Er*, YES. AFTER WE'VE SECURED THE SAMPLE..."

"...WE MAY AS WELL POKE AROUND A BIT AND SEE IF STREIB HAS ANYTHING *ELSE* OF INTEREST KICKING AROUND THE BIOLABS."

"AFTER ALL, HE HAD ACTUAL *BIOWEAPONS* RIGHT ON PACIFICA, VIRTUALLY UNDER GOLDIN'S *NOSE*.

7C BIOWEAPON STORAGE (HYPERGANGRE

7C

"ACTUALLY I'D BE RATHER SURPRISED IF HE *DIDN'T* HAVE A PILE OF NOXIOUS SUBSTANCES STORED IN THE BASE.

7C

"SO, WITH ANY LUCK, WE CAN LOCATE SOME DOWNRIGHT *DAMNING* EVIDENCE TO NAIL HIM WITH."

"JUST SO LONG AS *THIS ONE* ISN'T IN A *BREAKABLE* CONTAINER, *Hmm*?"

"AH...YES, SORRY ABOUT THAT, YURI."

"STILL, REGARDLESS OF OUR EFFORTS, WE'RE *BOUND* TO BE DISCOVERED AT SOME POINT...

VZZZ

"...AND THAT ISN'T GOING TO PLEASE STREIB VERY MUCH."
"AW, GEE... THAT'S JUST--"
--TOO BAD!
WOULD'VE BEEN NICE TO GET A LITTLE FURTHER!
HEY--
AIRLOCK
B
WE'VE GOT MY TISSUE SAMPLES...
...AND A WHOLE TANK OF "HYPERGANGRENE™" BIOAGENT...
...WHAT MORE COULD YOU ASK FOR?
JUST ONE THING--
--DON'T DROP THAT *¢%!ø ING TANK!

92

...TECH...

...TECH, DO YOU READ ME...?

AH. GOOD.

MR. STREIB IS CURRENTLY *DISINTEGRATING.*

O'DONNELL AND THOSE... THOSE *TWO* ARE PROBABLY ENROUTE TO THE SHUTTLE PAD.

KINDLY ASSEMBLE A QUICK AMBUSH AND *ERADICATE* THEM, IF YOU WOULD.

HMM? OH, I HAVE MY *OWN* PLANS.

BUT *PLEASE--*

"--DON'T *COMPLETELY* ATOMIZE THEM...

VRRNNNNn

"...BECAUSE I REQUEST THE SIMPLE PLEASURE OF *JUMPING* UP AND DOWN ON THEIR *BODIES.* "

READY...

KCHAK

KLAK

CHIK

FIRE.

BAM BAM KCHOW

THEY'RE *NOT* IN THE CAR...

THEY MUST HAV--

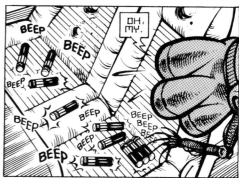

BEEP
BEEP
BEEP
BEEP
BEEP
BEEP
BEEP
BEEP
BEEP
BEEP BEEP BE

OH, MY.

≥ KOFF ≤

WELL, NOW...

...AREN'T YOU *GLAD* THAT WE SAVED OUR GRENADES BY USING MY BLOODY CA--

GIVE IT A *REST*, YURI--

-- I *ADMIT* IT WORKED, ALL RIGHT?

SCREEEEEEEEEEEEEEEEEEEEEEE

SAY... ...SOUNDS LIKE THE MAIN GUIDE TRACKS FOR THE WHEEL GOT SCREWED UP BY THOSE GRENADES...

SO LET'S GET *OUT* OF HERE!

GOOD IDEA, YURI...

...ESPECIALLY SINCE IT'S *MY* TURN TO DRIVE!

HEEEY!

SCREEEEEEEEEEEEEEEEEEEEEEEEEE

YOU WERE THE ONE FLYING THE GUNSHIP THAT LAST TIME...!

Oh, *NO,* I WASN'T!

YOU FLEW THE GUNSHIP IN THE CITY, REMEMBER?

BUT... BUT I *DON'T* REMEMBER!

I WAS FLIPPED OUT ON THAT *BIOAGENT*--

STREIB CO

--SO *THAT* DOESN'T COUNT! *NO FAIR!!*

103

MROWR?

KELVIN! ARE YOU OKAY?!

OHHHH

ATTENTION, 3WA VESSEL LOVELY ANGEL...

...PREPARE FOR *BOARDING* BY PACIFICA GLOBAL SECURITY. ATTENTION, 3WA VES--

PACIFICA GLOBAL SECURITY

HE'S UNDER ARREST?!?!

PGS

WHA--

WHY, *YES.* MR. O'DONNELL HAS BEEN *MANUFACTURING* BIOWEAPONS, YOU SEE.

SAVE YOUR PROTESTS FOR THE TRIAL, PLEASE.

I...

PGS

WHILE YOU WERE OUT CHASING AFTER STREIB--AND REMOVING HIS OPERATION AS A PROBLEM FOR US-- WE QUIETLY MOVED IN AND SHUT DOWN YOUR LABS ON BOTH *PACIFICA* AND *TALLIS.*

THE EVIDENCE WE FOUND WHILE CLEANING UP AFTER STREIB'S IDIOTIC SCENE IN THE CAPITAL FINALLY GAVE US THE LEVERAGE WE NEEDED TO FORCE THE GOVERNMENT TO ACT.

WITH THE 3WA INVOLVED--AND I'VE CLEARED THIS ALL WITH THEM, LADIES, DON'T YOU WORRY--AND BOTH STREIB AND YOU BUSY, I FIGURED THIS *WAS* MY CHANCE TO ACT WITHOUT A *BIOWEAPONS* INCIDENT.

OF COURSE, WE'LL GROW YOU YOUR *CLONE BODY*--

--AFTER ALL, A *WARBEAST* HARDLY MAKES AN IDEAL PRISONER.

BUT I'M AFRAID YOU'RE LOOKING AT A GOOD *TWO HUNDRED* YEARS FOR YOUR PLANT ON *TALLIS*...

YOU

...EVEN THOUGH WE FOUND NO BIOWEAPONS IN YOUR *PACIFICA* LAB, SO...

USED

US!!

WHOK

KEI! DON'T!

HE MAY *DESERVE* A MAIMING, BUT I DON'T WANT YOU IN THE CELL NEXT TO ME!

B-BUT...

HE *USED* US... TO...

LIK...

...CATCH YOU... ≥Snff≤

WELL, I APOLOGIZE FOR THE WHOLE MESS...

...BUT REALLY, IT'S NOT *YOUR* FAULT, KEI.

ANYWAY. I STILL LIKE YOU.

≥Snff≤

≥snff≤ BY *NODE*...

≥SNFF≤

=Snff=

=Snff=

Oh, COME ON NOW, KEI...

CHEER UP.

AT LEAST YOU DIDN'T *SCARE* HIM AWAY, LIKE YOU DO WITH *MOST* MEN...

WHAAT?!!

JUST *KIDDING*...

ALSO--*THIS TIME,* WE HARDLY LOST *ANY* INNOCENT BYSTANDERS!

=Snff=

YEAH... THAT'S TRUE...

Gee, YURI... I CAN SEE IT NOW--

"THE PEOPLE OF PACIFICA SAY:

"WE'RE *GLAD* THE LOVELY ANGELS DROPPED BY!"

THE END

I *love* hard science fiction. The ***Dirty Pair***, being essentially a space opera, may not seem very fertile ground for accurate, extrapolative scientific concepts, but one of the benefits of being a science fiction writer as opposed to a scientist is that one can fiddle with reality in the service of a better story.

Realistically, the world of 2141 is going to be rather different than that inhabited by the Lovely Angels. Advances in science and technology are going to render society even 100 years from now all but incomprehensible to someone raised in the latter half of the 20th century. Excellent examples are the burgeoning science of bioengineering and its inevitable spinoff, molecular engineering. As recently as 1959, many geneticists were saying that genetic engineering was impossible; today, it is an industry. Our control of protein mechanisms such as restriction enzymes has allowed us to custom-engineer bacteria that perform such useful tasks as secreting human insulin molecules. As our knowledge increases, we will soon be able to design protein machines from scratch. These tiny machines will then be directed to build even smaller machines, from sturdier materials than proteins. Millions of times smaller than anything we work with today, the capabilities of these mechanisms will be mind-boggling.

Examples? How about a computer with a billion bytes of storage that fits in a box a micron wide (about the size of a bacterium) working at 500,000 operations per second? How about a vat-grown rocket engine made of diamond honeycomb—with built-in AI and self-repair—made by dumping a few gallons of molecular machines into a tank filled with sugar water and carbon dust? How about cell-repairing machines smaller than a bacterium that will travel through your bloodstream and CSF not only attacking disease, but repairing trauma damage and the effects of aging? *Real* science fiction, you say? Not at all—in fact, most scientists consider these things inevitable, the end results of a progress as inexorable as that which has developed computers

from room-sized monsters with 2kb of storage to desktop iltralites with 80mb.

The effect that just this one branch of science is going to have on the near future is mind-boggling. Certainly, it will have an effect equal to or greater than that of the replacement of stone tools with metal ones, or the harnessing of electricity. The AI results of molecular processors will have a further effect on us that can only be compared to the effects of the development of language and writing, and these changes will take place, if not in your lifetime, then certainly within that of your children. So what hope can we have of understanding the world of 2141? Not very much, I'm afraid... but that doesn't make much of a story.

Like other SF writers, Adam and I have built our own future, one that we can understand and enjoy. We've tried to explore future science in a controllable manner—in selected bits and pieces, applied in hyper-specific ways. Let's face it: harsh reality makes lousy stories—who wants to see a *real* space battle, which would probably be fought by self-aware computers at distances of hundreds of thousands of miles, with actions taking place in an eye-blink? I'm reminded of TV news footage I saw of a Soviet fighter being shot down by a Stinker missile: the plane was a distant and near-invisible glint in the sky, the missile was fired, and eventually the guy with the binoculars said he thought he saw a parachute. Ho hum... hardly *Top Gun*! So reality is adjusted to make for an entertaining tale. And that's the way it needs to be.

What with the Pair themselves being the result of bio-engineering, biotechnology will probably continue to play a large part in the series as we see it. Shasti, from *Dirty Pair II*, is a result of several long conversations about the probable end result of the level of bioengineering used to produce Kei and Yuri themselves. The warbeasts from ***Biohazards*** are something I dreamed up myself, although the end design is Adam's; in my original script, I just said they were "mostly fangs, claws, and armor," a

CHARACTER SKETCHES
BY ADAM WARREN

description that fits Adam's design perfectly, I think! There's more to the warbeasts than meets the eye—a number of things about them never discussed or just touched upon in the series. I imagine most readers notice the warbeasts have several sets of eyes, the intent being that they would thus be damned difficult to sneak up on. Mechanical lenses are used simply for their greater durability. The armor is semi-organic, containing Kevlar-like polymers combined with sintered titanium carbide particles. The muscles are a combination of improved standard muscle tissues and *resilin*, a super-elastic protein used by such creatures as grasshoppers. The 'beasts' fighting reflexes are hardwired, which is to say not *learned* but *programmed* into the nervous system. O'Donnell's 'beast had several unique improvements: infrared "pits," like those in a pit viper for night ops, and generally improved image processing systems; the skeleton was mentioned as being HGC-based (and, in case you were wondering, HGC is a chemical that allows bones to soften). This would permit the 'beast to squeeze through incredibly tight spaces. The palms of the hands and soles of the feet can exude a complex protein called *glycocalix*, which is one of the stickiest substances known. By alternating it with an enzyme that dissolves it, climbing almost any sort of surface would be possible. By the way, to allow the hands to manipulate delicate devices, the fingers can be removed from the armor plating, which hinges back out of the way.

One of the problems with nervous systems as they have developed in complex carbon-based life is that they rely on chemical reactions at the synaptic junctions. These are slow, slow, slow. O'Donnell's warbeast uses copper "nerves" controlled by molecular computers. What kind of improvement would this make? Well, human nerve impulses travel about 0.2 miles per second—electrical impulses through copper wire move at about 186,000 miles per second.

One of the other gizmos I'm rather fond of is "Mughi's little black box," mentioned in Chapter 2. It uses induction to detect what's going inside a wire, then sort of insinuates itself into the system by mimicking the system's own signals. Once in, it gives the systems what it wants—regardless of what any outraged external sensors may be

saying. Similar systems are being used today in military ECM, for jamming enemy fire control radars, etc.

Adam is a big cyberpunk fan—as am I, for that matter. Hence the addition of computer interface plug sockets on both girls, behind their right ears. This, too, is an inevitable result of improvements in technology—let's face it: keyboards are a *joke*!

Weaponry is another fun field. Masamune Shirow (creator of *Appleseed*) has commented quite shrewdly on the guilty pleasures of weapons design, and I'll echo those sentiments here. Yeah, they're used for killing people, and that's pretty disgusting—but, on the other hand, there is seductive elegance in their efficiency. Besides, although it's not a popular viewpoint in modern liberal society, I believe there are some people who desperately *deserve* to be stamped out like scuttling cockroaches. In any case, Adam has thrown in a bunch of pretty interesting weapons. Check out the room full of bad guys in Chapter 2—see the guy on the extreme right wearing a spotted headband? It's hard to make out, but that's a "chain-knife" he's holding. I mean, why not?

An alternative cover for the first issue of *Dirty Pair*. Note the different logo, which Studio Proteus rejected in favor of the current gun-shot logo.

A lot of the guns are based on or extrapolated from extant weapons designs, like the gun Kei takes control of three pages later. That's based on the Calico M-950, a 9mm pistol with a magazine capacity of 50 to 100 rounds, using a helical mag. This one uses caseless ammo, though—just the propellant and a bullet, so there is no case to extract or eject after firing. The various weapons use a mix of methods to achieve their purpose of transmitting kinetic energy to the target, such as subcaliber flechette rounds. These were originally tested by the Army many years ago as part of the brilliant, but terminally screwed-up, SPIW program (which is finally being semi-revived with the consideration of the Steyr fischette weapon in

Another preliminary cover sketch for *Dirty Pair* #1. Interestingly, the sketches reproduced here, placed beside the final cover seem to comprise a complete fight sequence. Give it a try!

upcoming trials.) A flechette round is a projectile shaped like a tiny arrow, made of steel or tungsten, and weighing about 1/50th of an ounce (compared to regular bullets, which weigh upwards of 1/2 an ounce.) These are fired with *sabots*, which surround and grip the flechette, allowing it to be pushed down the barrel by expanding gases. The flechette leaves the sabot barrel at speeds in excess of 4.500 feet per second (about Mach 4). At that speed, a 1/50 oz. steel flechette will penetrate 1/2" armor plating. Flechette performance can be improved in different ways, such as that in one of Yuri's guns. Her flechettes use depleted uranium instead of steel for improved armor-piercing ability, and are propelled by a mag-netic railgun system to 16.000 fps (about Mach 14.) The sabots are partly ferrous metal, giving the magnetic fields something to adhere to.

This is getting a little long, but I'd like to mention the "Wheel," as seen in Chapter 4. This was designed in response to the problem of working on a moon with marginal gravity. What about artificial gravity, you ask? Well, in our 2141, that kind of technology is still very, very expensive and requires terrific amounts of energy when used over any sort of large area (although it's

fine for small areas like the decks of spacecraft). A cheaper solution, and the one used by Streib, is centripetal force. In space, such a construction would have floors perfectly perpendicular to the plane of motion. However, to compensate for the gravitational force vector of the moon Telek, the floors have to be angled slightly. This causes the vectors to balance, and produce a perceived total "ver-tical" acceleration of 1g.

That's enough, I think. Oh—just one last comment: you can stop writing to us about Yuri's boot switching feet throughout Chapter 3. We know, we know.

Best,

Toren Smith

This third preliminary cover sketch reveals Adam's fine sense of composition and motion. Kei is in the act of drawing down on the warbeast before her.

MANGA VIDEO

If you've enjoyed this Manga Book, you'll love the animated movies and series released on the Manga Video label. Many of them are based on Japanese comics (*Crying Freeman, Akira* and *Battle Angel Alita* to name but a few), but all of them prove that there are no limits to animation with their imaginings of post-apocalyptic hells, bio-engineered mechanoids, other-worldly nightmarish fiends, wide-eyed babes, devouring tentacles and neon techno-mad cities. The range of Manga Videos is available from all good video and record stores including Virgin, HMV, Woolworths, WH Smith, Our Price, Playhouse and Forbidden Planet, and there are new titles out every month.

To find out more, join the Official Manga Club and receive a quarterly newsletter, as well as discounts on Manga Books and selected Manga Videos, free entry to competitions, free Manga merchandise and a free copy of the Manga Video Collectors Edition (retail price £6.99) — all for only £10 a year. Call 0181 563 2028 for an application form, or fill out and send off the form available in every Manga Video.

Up-to-date news on Manga is also available on the Internet by accessing **http://www.mangavid.co.uk/mangavid** or **http://www.mangapub.co.uk/mangapub/**

If you're new to Japanese animation, then these are some of the most popular titles:

AKIRA
(15 cert., 124 mins approx., #IWCV 1001, RRP: £13.99)

Drug-crazed biker gangs battle for high-speed supremacy in the neonscape of a nightmare future Tokyo: this is the setting for the biggest, most expensively produced and most famous manga release ever.

UROTSUKIDOJI: LEGEND OF THE OVERFIEND
(18 cert, 104 mins approx., #MANV 1008, RRP: £13.99)

& LEGEND OF THE DEMON WOMB
(18 cert, 83 mins approx., #MANV 1009, RRP: £13.99)

Terrifying masterpieces beyond the limits of animation as demonic lusts and super-natural ultraviolence explode into physical reality.

THE GUYVER
(12 episodes, RRP: £5.99, all approx. 30 mins)

An epic science fiction adventure which explores the fusion of man and machine, and delves into the origins of the human species itself.

DOMINION TANK POLICE
(8 videos - 2 @ 68 mins approx., RRP: £13.99 and 6 @ 30 mins approx., RRP: £5.99)

Riotous tales of police, pollution and heavy weaponry from cybermeister Masamune Shirow, set in a world where the cops are more dangerous than the crooks!

FIST OF THE NORTH STAR
(18 cert, 112 mins approx., #MANV 1001, RRP: £13.99)

A grim-faced lone warrior, armed with the power of an age-old martial arts discipline, wanders the ruined and irradiated waste-lands of a post-apocalyptic nuclear hell, searching for the woman he loves and pro-tecting mankind's final chance for survival.

PATLABOR
(PG cert, 99 mins approx., #MANV 1080, RRP: £13.99)

An incredibly animated science fiction drama set against a tale of danger and hi-tech revenge as the police force of 1999 enlist advanced pilot-operated robots to combat crime.